God's Rules for Me

Coloring and Activity Book

Written and illustrated by
Virginia Helen Richards, FSP and D. Thomas Halpin, FSP

Pauline

BOOKS & MEDIA

Boston

Rules! Rules! Rules!
Rules are everywhere.

Do you know
why we have rules?

Rules keep us safe,
just as the traffic light does,

or as the crosswalks do.

By obeying rules
we stay safe and happy.

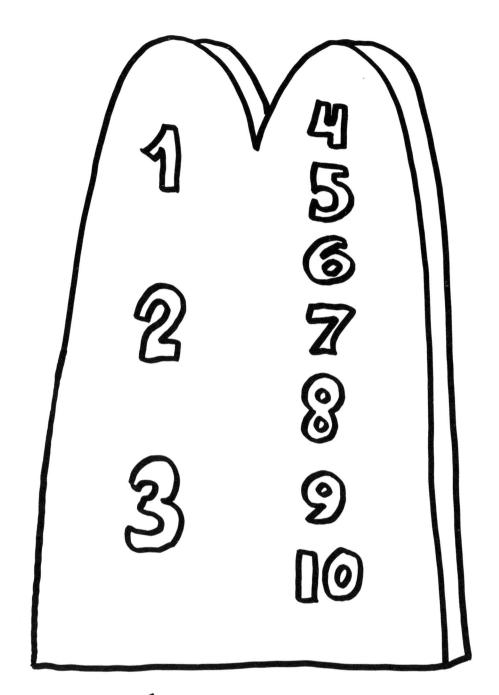

There are some rules
that are the *most* important of all.

They are God's rules.

They are called the

Ten Commandments.

The first 3 commandments
are about **God** and **us.**

The other 7 commandments
are about *other people* and *us.*

Like the rules in the games we play,
God's rules teach us
how to live happily.

1 God's first rule:
Love God.

God is great.
God is good.
I will love him as I should!

2, God's second rule:
Honor God's name.

I will pray
with great love,

for God's name
is blest above.

3 God's third rule:
Keep God's day holy

Sunday is a holy day.

We worship God
in a special way.

God's fourth rule:

4 Be obedient.

Every day
I'll obey

16

those who guide me
in God's way.

5 God's fifth rule:

Be kind.

I am kind.
I won't fight.

Hurting others
is not right.

6 God's sixth rule:
Be pure.

My body is
a blessing true.

God lives in me
and others too!

7 God's seventh rule:

Respect what belongs to others.

I won't take
what's not mine.

I'll return
the things I find.

God's eighth rule:

Be truthful.

I won't lie.
I'll be true…

24

saying only
good things, too.

9 & 10

God's ninth and tenth rules:

Be at peace

With my things
I'm satisfied.

and satisfied.

I don't want
what isn't mine.

I will pray well
every day

that God's rules
I may obey.

God's rules bring
a great **reward**...

Life in heaven
with our **Lord!**

31

Find the way!

Find your way to the Ten Commandments.
They are the road to happiness!

Start

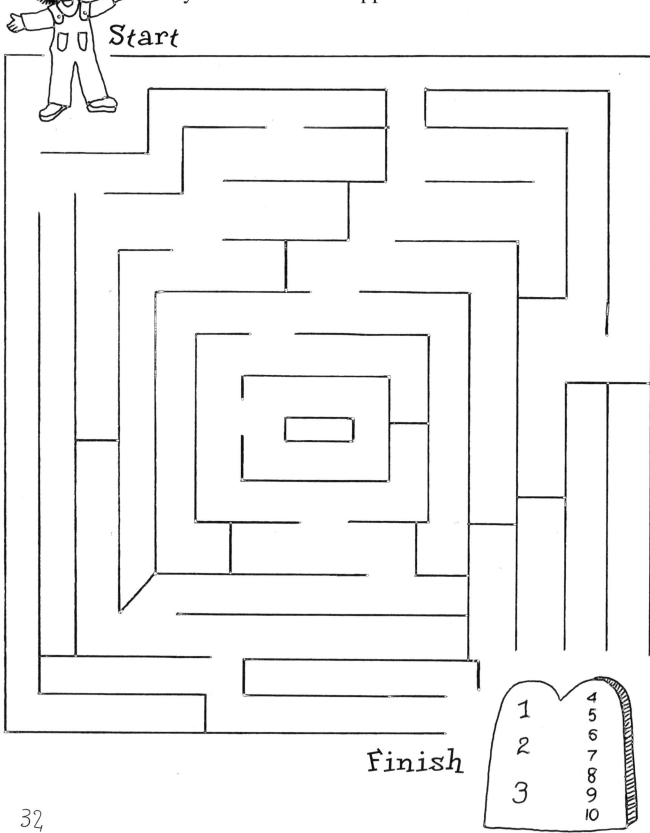

Finish

32